JOURNEY 101
STEPS TO THE LIFE GOD INTENDS

SERVING GOD

Participant Guide

JOURNEY 101
STEPS TO THE LIFE GOD INTENDS

This three-part basic faith course is designed to teach what it means to know, love, and serve God. Each of the three separate, interactive six-week studies uses a group-teaching format, combining video teaching and small-group table breakouts. The three studies include:

KNOWING GOD. Explore the good news of the Bible and discover Bible study tools and resources to deepen your understanding of God and the Scriptures.

LOVING GOD. Experience spiritual transformation through spiritual practices that will help you fall more in love with God and grow in your relationship with God and others.

SERVING GOD. Understand the biblical context for service that will enable you to use your hands, your time, and your spiritual gifts to serve others and share Christ.

COMPONENTS

Participant Guide (one for each study)—Each includes interactive guides for six sessions with space for responding to questions and activities and recording personal reflections.

Leader Guide (one for each study)—Each includes complete session guides with leader helps for facilitating a six-week study.

Journey 101 Daily Readings—Serves as the devotional companion for the entire three-part Journey 101 series. Ninety devotions (thirty devotions per study).

DVD—Three-disc set (120 minutes per DVD/study; 360 minutes total).

Preview Book—Provides an overview of the topics covered in the entire three-part Journey 101 course.

Leader Kit—One each of the components listed above.

SERVING GOD

PARTICIPANT GUIDE

Carol Cartmill
Jeff Kirby
Michelle Kirby

Abingdon Press

Nashville

JOURNEY 101: SERVING GOD
Participant Guide

Copyright © 2013 by Abingdon Press

This book is printed on acid-free paper.

ISBN 978-1-4267-6586-5

13 14 15 16 17 18 19 20 21 22—10 9 8 7 6 5 4 3 2 1

MANUFACTURED IN THE UNITED STATES OF AMERICA

Projects like this are never created in a vacuum. The work represented here is built on five years of offering this course to the members of our home church. We would like to recognize the contributions of so many at The United Methodist Church of the Resurrection who helped to lead, facilitate and shape this study, especially: Jonathan Bell, Susan Campbell, Nicole Conard, Gia Garey-Moser, Darren Lippe, Debi Nixon, David Robertson, Chuck Russell, and Clayton Smith. We dedicate this study to them.

CONTENTS

CONTENTS

Introduction

THE JOURNEY

When we give our lives to Jesus Christ and commit to follow him, we embark on a lifelong journey of knowing, loving, and serving God. Growing as a Christian and becoming a committed follower of Jesus Christ means . . .

knowing God by becoming theologically informed,

loving God and experiencing spiritual transformation, and

serving God by using our hands to serve others and share Christ.

Journey 101 is a three-part course designed to help guide us on this journey of knowing, loving, and serving God. As we embark on this journey, it is vitally important that we know the destination, the place where we want to end up. And that destination is to become deeply committed Christians—people who know, love, and serve God with increasing passion and dedication. As we journey toward this destination, the studies in this series will help us to answer some important questions:

- How does a deeply committed Christian grow to know God more deeply?

- How would our lives be transformed if we loved God with the fullness of our hearts?

- How should we, as deeply committed Christians, be serving in the world?

To help us know that we are on the right track to our destination, we have identified fifteen markers to guide us along the way. We call these markers the fifteen core traits of a deeply committed Christian. These traits paint a picture of what it looks like to live as a deeply committed follower of Jesus Christ. Each study in the Journey 101 series focuses on five of these core traits. (See pages 12–13 for detailed descriptions of these core traits.)

Because starting any journey can sometimes be daunting, particularly if you find yourself in unfamiliar territory or surroundings, Journey 101 serves as a navigation system that provides directions, routes, and traveling companions to support and encourage you along the way. Here is what you can expect to learn in each of the three studies:

KNOWING GOD

- Gain a better understanding of the essentials of the Christian faith.
- Experience new Bible study tools and resources.
- Discover more about the church.
- Discuss ethics and our Christian response to life's decisions.
- Understand more about God's will for your life.

LOVING GOD

- Learn about the Holy Spirit's transforming power in our lives.
- Understand more about what it means to love God with all your heart, soul, mind, and strength and to love your neighbor as you love yourself (Luke 10:27).
- Understand and experience key spiritual practices including Bible study, prayer, worship, fasting, guidance, and journaling.
- Learn to recognize the "fruit" of God's transforming activity in our lives—love, joy, peace, patience, kindness, generosity, gentleness, faithfulness, and self-control.

SERVING GOD

- Focus on the Bible's concern for the poor and for justice while learning how to be instruments of God's love in a broken, hurting world.
- Learn how to share the good news of Jesus in loving, winsome, and non-judgmental ways.

- Understand spiritual gifts and talents and how to use those gifts to bless others and build up the body of Christ.

- Learn how our money and material possessions are not a measure of success or a means of self-gratification, but a resource to responsibly use to glorify God.

- View time as a gift from God, to be used in keeping with God's purposes, avoiding compulsive busyness and submitting our calendars to God's guiding and control.

Although it is recommended that you take each of these studies, there is no set order in which you must complete them.

WHAT TO EXPECT

Journey 101 is designed as an in-class experience. In other words, everything takes place in the group setting. There is no homework to be done outside of class. This participant guide serves as your "map" for the weekly group experience. You will need to bring it with you to each class, along with a pen or pencil and a Bible. (If you forget your Bible or don't own one, there will be extras available.)

Each week you will spend time connecting with those in your group, reflecting on where you are on your journey, viewing and discussing several video segments, reviewing what you have learned, and praying together. Simply follow along in your participant guide as your leader guides you through the session. Questions and activities that you are to answer or complete in your book are highlighted in bold type. Share your answers to the discussion questions as a group, taking notes in your participant guide as you move through the questions together. Whether you write a little or a lot, your participant guide will become your own personal record of your journey and the insights you gain along the way.

Though no homework is involved, you may wish to use the devotional companion, *Journey 101 Daily Readings*, in your private devotions while completing the three-part Journey 101 series. These devotions will help to enrich your understanding and application of what you are learning in class.

We believe that nothing in the world will bring you greater joy, greater challenge, and greater meaning than the journey into life as God intended us to live it. As you begin the journey, open yourself to what God has to teach you through the Scriptures, prayer, and the guidance of the Holy Spirit.

FIFTEEN CORE TRAITS OF A DEEPLY COMMITTED CHRISTIAN

KNOWING GOD

Christian Essentials—Deeply committed Christians understand the essential gospel on which most Christians agree, across denominational lines and centuries, expressed in historic creeds such as the Apostles' and Nicene creeds, and can share the gospel intelligently with non-Christian friends.

Bible Understanding—Deeply committed Christians know the grand sweep of the Bible's story of salvation, including a basic time line of biblical events. They understand the divine/human nature of the Bible and know how to read it, not merely as an ancient document or a reference book of spiritual answers, but for personal spiritual growth.

Church/Denomination—Deeply committed Christians value the church as the body of Christ, God's people journeying in community, and know the teachings characteristic of their particular denomination.

Basic Christian Ethics—Deeply committed Christians understand how to apply their Christian faith to important ethical issues and are committed to living out Christian ethical principles such as justice, integrity, peace, and responsibility for the well-being of others.

Knowing God's Will—Deeply committed Christians know the broad scope of God's purpose for human beings, and have a growing sense of how to discern God's will for their lives through prayer, Bible study, and the wisdom of other Christians.

LOVING GOD

Surrender—Deeply committed Christians surrender the control of every aspect of their lives to Jesus, repent of sin, set aside their own desires and sense of importance, and offer their lives in obedient service to God.

Transformation—Deeply committed Christians are being continually transformed by the power of the Holy Spirit, and sense that power molding their values, priorities, and relationships into more Christlike patterns.

Spiritual Disciplines—Deeply committed Christians practice various spiritual disciplines (e.g., prayer, Bible reading, worship, solitude, meditation, fasting) as a means of surrendering to Jesus and opening their lives to the Holy Spirit's transforming activity.

Fruit of the Spirit—Deeply committed Christians are continually growing in the inner qualities and outward actions identified as "the fruit of the Spirit" in Galatians 5:22-23 (NRSV): "love, joy, peace, patience, kindness, generosity, faithfulness, gentleness, and self-control."

Authentic Community—Deeply committed Christians share their faith journeys with groups of Christian friends in mutual encouragement and accountability, developing spiritual honesty and trust through sharing and support.

SERVING GOD

Service to Others—Deeply committed Christians are instruments of God's love in a broken, hurting world, living lives of service to others with a strong (though not exclusive) focus on the Bible's concern for the poor and for justice.

Sharing Christ—Deeply committed Christians are eager to share the good news of Jesus in loving, winsome, and non-judgmental ways, and are ready to "give an answer to everyone who asks you to give the reason for the hope that you have" (1 Peter 3:15).

Spiritual Gifts/Talents—Deeply committed Christians understand clearly with "sober judgment" (Romans 12:3) which spiritual gifts and talents they have, and use those gifts to bless others and build up the body of Christ.

Financial Gifts—Deeply committed Christians view money and material possessions not as a measure of success or as a means of self-gratification, but as a resource for whose use they are responsible to God, and submit their financial lives to God's guiding and control.

Time—Deeply committed Christians see time as a gift from God to be used in keeping with God's purposes, avoid compulsive busyness, and submit their calendars to God's guiding and control.

HOW AND WHY WE SERVE GOD

Jesus went through all the towns and villages, teaching in their synagogues, proclaiming the good news of the kingdom and healing every disease and sickness.

Matthew 9:35

CORE TRAIT

- Service to Others

WELCOME

Welcome to *Journey 101: Serving God*. Through this study you will explore what it means to serve God as God's disciples. In order to know how to serve God, we first must discover what is important to God; and to do this, we can look to Jesus. We serve God by doing the things that Jesus did: loving others by acting with justice, mercy, compassion, and care. In this session, you'll learn that every journey with God leads to other people.

CONNECT

Discuss the following questions and suggestions with your group to get to know one another better and get the conversation started.

- Meet the people around your table. Share your name and how long you have attended this church.

- Find three things that everyone at your table has in common with one another.

- In what era—if other than your own—do you wish you had grown up? Why?

- If it were possible for you to do something dangerous just once without risk, what would you do?

- If you had the means, how would you address the problem of homelessness?

In the space that follows, write the names of people you have met in your group and one thing about each of them that you learned in conversation. This will help you remember names and get to know one another a little more.

REFLECT

Here, at the beginning of your study, reflect on your understanding of what it means to serve. How do you feel about serving as opposed to being the one served? Take an assessment of your willingness and availability to serve by marking the scale below and completing the sentence.

Sign me up!   Let me get back to you...   I can't do that!

| 1 | 2 | 3 | 4 | 5 | 6 | 7 | 8 | 9 | 10 |

For me, serving God means . . .

1 VIDEO HIGHLIGHTS: JOURNEYING WITH GOD LEADS TO OTHER PEOPLE

Then God said, "Let us make humanity in our image to resemble us so that they may take charge of the fish of the sea, the birds of the sky, the livestock, all the earth, and all the crawling things on earth."
Genesis 1:26 CEB

- Every journey with God leads to other people.

- "Our" = Father, Son, Holy Spirit.

- Right from the beginning, God introduces the concept of community.

- God made Adam and Eve, who had Cain and Abel and Seth—community.

- We are meant to be dependent on one another.

- We survive by sharing our gifts and talents with others—that's the way God created us to be.

- Joseph was led away from his family but toward God.

  The LORD was with Joseph.
  Genesis 39:2a

- Joseph was on a journey that led to community.

- When we commit to following God, we can be sure that we will be doing it in community.

1 GROUP DISCUSSION

1. Name some examples of how you experience community in your life (family, friends, church, the workplace, other).

2. Have someone read aloud part of Joseph's story found in Genesis 45:1-15. How did Joseph's journey lead to community?

3. What does it mean that we were created to be dependent on one another?

4. How do all journeys with God lead to community?

---

2 VIDEO HIGHLIGHTS: LEARN ABOUT SERVING FROM JESUS

"For even the Son of Man did not come to be served, but to serve, and to give his life as a ransom for many."
Mark 10:45

- If you want to see God, look to Jesus. Jesus is God with skin on.

- In story after story in the Gospels, Jesus is serving—healing others, teaching, raising people from the dead, comforting.

Soon afterward, Jesus went to a town called Nain, and his disciples and a large crowd went along with him. As he approached the town gate, a dead person was being carried out—the only son of his mother, and she was a widow. And a large crowd from the town was with her. When the Lord saw her, his heart went out to her and he said, "Don't cry."

Then he went up and touched the bier they were carrying him on, and the bearers stood still. He said, "Young man, I say to you, get up!" The dead man sat up and began to talk, and Jesus gave him back to his mother.

They were all filled with awe and praised God. "A great prophet has appeared among us," they said. "God has come to help his people." This news about Jesus spread throughout Judea and the surrounding country.

Luke 7:11-17

- Compassion means to suffer alongside someone.

- Jesus' heart broke and then he acted. He healed people because he loved them and loved serving them.

- Jesus was downwardly mobile—a carpenter who preached, taught, healed, served; a working king.

Jesus called them together and said, "You know that those who are regarded as rulers of the Gentiles lord it over them, and their high officials exercise authority over them. Not so with you. Instead, whoever wants to become great among you must be your servant, and whoever wants to be first must be slave of all. For even the Son of Man did not come to be served, but to serve, and to give his life as a ransom for many."
Mark 10:42-45

- When we follow Christ we want to look like him; what does that mean?

  ○ He looks like a servant who comes to serve.

  ○ He looks like the face of compassion. (When he sees people suffering, his heart breaks.)

  ○ He teaches about God and what it looks like to live in God's kingdom.

Your attitude should be the same as that of Christ Jesus:
  Who, being in very nature God,
    did not consider equality with God something to be grasped,
  but made himself nothing,
    taking the very nature of a servant
    being made in human likeness.
  And being found in appearance as a man,
    he humbled himself
    and became obedient to death—
      even death on a cross!
  Therefore God exalted him to the highest place
    and gave him the name that is above every name,
  that at the name of Jesus every knee should bow,
    in heaven and on earth and under the earth,
  and every tongue confess that Jesus Christ is Lord,
    to the glory of God the Father.
Philippians 2:5-11 NIV 1984

- The way of Jesus is serving others—loving people the way that Jesus loved them.

2 GROUP DISCUSSION

1. What do you think it means that Jesus is "God with skin on"?

2. What do we know from Jesus' teaching and ministry about the importance of serving?

3. Have someone read aloud Luke 7:11-17. How does Jesus show compassion in this story? What does it tell us about his heart for hurting people?

4. When have you felt led to "suffer alongside" someone?

5. What would the world look like if all Christians lived out Jesus' example of serving?

6. How could you begin to serve like Jesus? To have compassion like Jesus? To love others like Jesus did?

7. Have someone read aloud Philippians 2:5-11. What is Jesus' attitude? How can we have the same attitude?

3   VIDEO HIGHLIGHTS: THE CHURCH SERVES

The believers devoted themselves to the apostles' teaching, to the community, to their shared meals, and to their prayers. A sense of awe came over everyone. God performed many wonders and signs through the apostles. All the believers were united and shared everything. They would sell pieces of property and possessions and distribute the proceeds to everyone who needed them. Every day, they met together in the temple and ate in their homes. They shared food with gladness and simplicity. They praised God and demonstrated God's goodness to everyone. The Lord added daily to the community those who were being saved.

Acts 2:42-47 CEB

- We need one another to serve in community.
- The early church identified themselves as servants—being the hands and feet of Jesus in the world. They:
    - brought health and healing to a hurting world;
    - took care of orphans and widows—those who couldn't care for themselves;
    - preached about Christ, sharing the good news of the kingdom of God; and
    - prayed for people's physical, emotional, and spiritual sicknesses.
- Our goal as the church is to continue the work of Christ.
- We don't have to look very far to find people in need.
- We should be moved and compelled to serve as Jesus did.
- We identify a need—prompted by a broken heart.
- Knowing God = Showing God.
- John Wesley believed it is as important to live out one's faith as to profess it. He knew that suffering and need had to be addressed before the good news would have meaning.

One great reason why the rich in general have so little sympathy for the poor is because they so seldom visit them.[1]
—John Wesley

- Wesley believed that everything we have is a gift from God and anything that is surplus is to be given to the poor.

Scriptures on Serving

But if a person has material possessions and sees a brother or sister in need and that person doesn't care—how can the love of God remain in him?

Little children, let's not love with words or speech but with action and truth.

1 John 3:17-18 CEB

Brothers and sisters, because of God's mercies, I encourage you to present your bodies as a living sacrifice that is holy and pleasing to God.

Romans 12:1a CEB

Speak up for those who cannot speak for themselves,
for the rights of all who are destitute.
Speak up and judge fairly;
defend the rights of the poor and needy.

Proverbs 31:8-9

The place God calls you to is the place where your deep gladness and the world's deep hunger meet.[2]
—Frederick Buechner

- Risks of doing good:
  - control
  - rejection
  - misuse
  - self-denial
  - fear

- Results of doing good:
  - ○ *Blessed are those who act justly, who always do what is right.* (Psalm 106:3)

  - ○ *If your enemy is hungry, give him food to eat; if he is thirsty, give him water to drink . . . and the LORD will reward you.* (Proverbs 25:21-22)

  - ○ *Do not be overcome by evil, but overcome evil with good.* (Romans 12:21)

- When we serve others, we are forever changed and our world is transformed.

3 GROUP DISCUSSION

1. How have you seen the church at work in service to your community?

2. Why is it important to serve as part of a community?

3. How do you respond to the ideas shared in the video about doing good and helping the poor? What challenges you? What appeals to you? Why?

4. Have someone read aloud James 2:14-18. In your experience, how does faith lead to works? How has your faith led you to do good?

5. Have someone read aloud Galatians 5:22–6:2. In these verses, Paul suggests that it is grace that empowers the practice of doing good, which in turn transforms the community. How has your Christian community been shaped by grace, and how has grace shaped your community's efforts to "do good" in the larger society?

6. **What are some ways you have practiced the rule to "do good"? What challenges have you identified in your efforts to practice this rule?**

REVIEW

In this session, the three main points were:

1.

2.

3.

How are you being led to serve?

CLOSING

In the last video segment you heard a story about how serving others changed Terri's life. When have you served someone and felt changed by the experience? Answer the following questions and then share with your group.

1. **When did serving someone change you?**

2. **What happened as a result of your act of service?**

3. **How is your life a response to that change in you?**

PRAY TOGETHER

Share joys and concerns among your group. Write down anything you are asked to pray for.

Lord Jesus, we thank you for your amazing love. We ask that you would reveal to us the great needs around us and move our hearts to "doing." Show us how to love and care for one another in the same ways you did. May our love and knowledge of you, Lord, continue to grow and change the world. In Jesus' name. Amen.

WALKING IT OUT

- Continue the journey by reflecting on the three main ideas of the session throughout the coming week:

  1. Every journey with God always leads to community.

  2. Jesus teaches us how to serve.

  3. We are called to serve the world as community—the church.

- In your personal prayer time:

  ○ give thanks for the ways that others have served you or shown you compassion;

  ○ acknowledge that you may not always see the world with the eyes of Christ; and

  ○ pray that you would have the eyes to see the world as God does, and look for ways to serve.

- Give more thought to the ways that serving others changes you. How can you be more aware of opportunities to serve?

- Spend time each day in personal devotion and prayer. You may want to use *Journey 101 Daily Readings* as a tool to guide your time with God.

SERVING WITH TIME

People can do nothing better than to eat and drink and find satisfaction in their toil. This too, I see, is from the hand of God.
Ecclesiastes 2:24 TNIV

CORE TRAIT

- Time

WELCOME

Do you ever feel that you don't have enough time—that if there were just a few more hours in the day, you could really feel good about your work? Or do you ever feel that time is wasted—that you should be getting things done instead of resting? You may not realize it, but how we use our time is a core trait of fully devoted disciples of Jesus Christ. Time matters, and how we use our time is of great concern to God. Using it wisely and prudently demonstrates our love of God and our obedience to God. In today's session, you'll make a plan to structure your time so that you have a healthy rhythm of life and remain available for God to work in and through you.

Connect

Discuss the following questions with your group to get to know one another better and get the conversation started.

- What is your favorite way to spend free time?
- If you had the ability to trade places with someone for a month, whom would you choose? Why?
- Which do you think is more essential to humanity, art or science? Why?
- Last week's lesson was on how and why we serve God. Have you experienced God speaking to you this week regarding ways you can serve?
- In your opinion, what do you think is the most significant problem facing our world?

In the space that follows, write the names of people you have met and one thing about each of them that you learned in conversation. This will help you remember names and get to know one another a little more.

Reflect

Today you are going to take a hard look at your time management and explore how to make the most of your time.

In the space below, make a list of your weekly engagements and commitments.

Circle the life-giving things. Put a box around the things that cause hurry or busyness.

As you look at your list, consider if you have any "free time" remaining in your schedule. If so, what could you do with this time?

1 VIDEO HIGHLIGHTS: STEWARDS OF TIME

God said, "Let there be light." And so light appeared.
Genesis 1:3 CEB

- Time is a part of God's creation—night and day—and we are called to be stewards of time.

- Time is a gift from God; it brings order to our lives.

  God blessed them and said to them, "Be fertile and multiply; fill the earth and master it. Take charge of the fish of the sea, the birds of the sky, and everything crawling on the ground."
  Genesis 1:28 CEB

- God put human beings in charge over creation, which includes time.

- Throughout the day we are given opportunities to do God's work in the world and to spend time with God. How are we using these opportunities of time?

- None of us wants to get to the end of our lives and say we wasted our time.

  Then he told them a parable: "A certain rich man's land produced a bountiful crop. He said to himself, What will I do? I have no place to store my harvest! Then he thought, Here's what I'll do. I'll tear down my barns and build bigger ones. That's where I'll store all my grain and goods. I'll say to myself, You have stored up plenty of goods, enough for several years. Take it easy! Eat, drink, and enjoy yourself. But God said to him, 'Fool, tonight you will die. Now who will get the things you have prepared for yourself?' This is the way it will be for those who hoard things for themselves and aren't rich toward God."
  Luke 12:16-21 CEB

- We are called to make the most of our present reality in time.

1 GROUP DISCUSSION

1. What do you think it means to be a good "steward" of your time?

2. Have you ever thought about stewarding your time in the same way that you steward your money or household? When is it easy to steward time? When is it difficult?

3. Have someone read aloud Luke 12:16-21. How does this parable speak to you about your priorities?

4. What does it look like to make the most of our "present reality in time"?

2 VIDEO HIGHLIGHTS: A HEALTHY RHYTHM OF LIFE

On the sixth day God completed all the work that he had done, and on the seventh day God rested from all the work that he had done. God blessed the seventh day and made it holy, because on it God rested from all the work of creation.
Genesis 2:2-3 CEB

- God demonstrates for us a healthy rhythm of life. The rhythm is set at Creation—first there is creation, then there is rest.

- We are commanded to practice Sabbath rest:

Remember the Sabbath day and treat it as holy.
Exodus 20:8 CEB

For six years you should plant crops on your land and gather in its produce. But in the seventh year you should leave it alone and undisturbed so that the poor among your people may eat. What they leave behind, the wild animals may eat. You should do the same with your vineyard and your olive trees.

Do your work in six days. But on the seventh day you should rest so that your ox and donkey may rest, and even the child of your female slave and the immigrant may be refreshed.

Exodus 23:10-12 CEB

- God knew that we would need rest.

- Jesus practiced Sabbath rest and honored the Sabbath.

Right then, Jesus made the disciples get into the boat and go ahead to the other side of the lake while he dismissed the crowds. When he sent them away, he went up onto a mountain by himself to pray. Evening came and he was alone.

Matthew 14:22-23 CEB

Early in the morning, well before sunrise, Jesus rose and went to a deserted place where he could be alone in prayer.

Mark 1:35 CEB

Jesus went to Nazareth, where he had been raised. On the Sabbath he went to the synagogue as he normally did and stood up to read.

Luke 4:16 CEB

- A hurried lifestyle is the enemy of a close relationship with God.

Ruthlessly eliminate hurry from your life.[1]

—John Ortberg

- We must learn to enjoy the fruits of our labor.

What do workers gain from all their hard work? I have observed the task that God has given human beings. God has made everything fitting in its time, but has also placed eternity in their hearts, without enabling them to discover what God has done from beginning to end.

I know that there's nothing better for them but to enjoy themselves and do what's good while they live. Moreover, this is the gift of God: that all people should eat, drink, and enjoy the results of their hard work. I know that whatever God does will last forever; it's impossible to add to it or take away from it. God has done this so that people are reverent before him. Whatever happens has already happened, and whatever will happen has already happened before. And God looks after what is driven away.

Ecclesiastes 3:9-15 CEB

- We can't control time, but we can control our attitude and our posture toward it.

2 GROUP DISCUSSION

1. Have someone read aloud Genesis 2:2-3. Why do you think God set the rhythm of time to include a day of rest?

2. Have someone read aloud Matthew 14:13-27. What do you think were some of Jesus' greatest challenges in creating some margin in his time?

3. Contrast Jesus' reactions to crises and demands with those of his disciples. How do they differ?

4. Describe the level of hurry in your life.

5. What would it take to ruthlessly eliminate hurry from your life?

6. Have someone read aloud all of Ecclesiastes 3. How does this passage challenge you to take hold of your time?

3 VIDEO HIGHLIGHTS: LOVING GOD AND OTHERS WITH OUR TIME

He replied, "You must love the Lord your God with all your heart, with all your being, and with all your mind. This is the first and greatest commandment. And the second is like it: You must love your neighbor as you love yourself."
Matthew 22:37-39 CEB

- Time is a resource we utilize in order to live out the two great commands of Jesus.

- It comes down to this: God gives us time—what are we doing with it? Are we using it wisely or wasting it?

- Are we loving God and serving others or focusing only on ourselves?

- We make time for what's important to us.

- Relationships can fall apart if we don't carve out time for one another.

- Our relationship with God suffers when we don't make time for it.

- God gives us the gift of time so that we can use it wisely to help others in need—which is a way we show our love for God and for others.

- Prescription for restoring margin in your life:

  Rx 1—Expect the unexpected.

  Rx 2—Learn to say no.

  Rx 3—Turn off the television.

  Rx 4—Prune the activity branches.

  Rx 5—Practice simplicity and contentment.

  Rx 6—Separate time from technology.

  Rx 7—Short-term flurry versus long-term vision.

  Rx 8—Thank God.

Rx 9—Sabotage your fuse box.

Rx 10—Get less done but do the right things.

Rx 11—Enjoy anticipation; relish the memories.

Rx 12—Don't rush wisdom.

Rx 13—For type As only: stand in line.

Rx 14—Create buffer zones.

Rx 15—Plan for free time.

Rx 16—Be available.[2]

We must be ready to allow ourselves to be interrupted by God. God will constantly be crossing our paths and canceling our plans by sending us people with claims and petitions. . . . It is part of the discipline of humility that we must not spare our hand where it can perform a service and that we do not assume that our schedule is our own to manage, but allow it to be arranged by God.[3]
—Dietrich Bonhoeffer

- God created time for our benefit. We are to be stewards of our time. Let's choose to invest our time by loving God and serving others.

3 GROUP DISCUSSION

1. **What are the barriers you face when it comes to using your time in ways that bless others?**

2. **Which of the "prescriptions for restoring time margin" would be most helpful to you? Why?**

3. **How do you relate to time in your day-to-day life—in both healthy and unhealthy ways?**

4. Reflect on a time when your heart wanted to help or serve in some way but you just couldn't find the time. How might you have been able to make time by cutting other things out of your schedule?

5. How is it true that God created time for our benefit? What are some of those benefits?

6. What adjustments can you make in your schedule in order to allow time for you to be "interrupted by God"?

REVIEW

In this session, the three main points were:

1.

2.

3.

CLOSING

In the final DVD segment you heard a story about Mary giving the gift of her time and making a difference in someone's life in a moment of need.

1. In what ways could you give your time to bless another person?

2. Brainstorm some ideas for giving the gift of time and make notes about how you would organize your time to make these things happen.

Pray Together

Share joys and concerns among your group. Write down anything you are asked to pray for.

God, thank you for the gift of time, and we thank you for showing us a rhythm for how we are to spend our time. We ask that your Holy Spirit will help us to use our time wisely, investing it in things that have meaning. Help us to be more available to you and to come into your presence to be refilled and refueled, just as Jesus modeled for us. Help us to take control of our calendars so that, when it really counts, we can be available to serve those that you place in our paths. In Jesus' name, we pray. Amen.

WALKING IT OUT

- Continue the journey by reflecting on the three main ideas of the session throughout the coming week:

    1. God created time, and we are stewards of it.

    2. God gave us a healthy rhythm of life.

    3. We can love God and love others with our time.

- In your personal prayer time:

    ○ give thanks for the gift of Sabbath,

    ○ acknowledge that you may have wasted time or opportunity to be a blessing,

    ○ seek forgiveness and ask God to give you focus as you manage your time, and

    ○ praise God for the opportunity to be a blessing to someone else.

- Give more thought to the ways that you can serve God with your time. How can you carve out time for God and time for serving others? How are you ruthlessly eliminating hurry from your days?

- Spend time each day in personal devotion and prayer. You may want to use *Journey 101 Daily Readings* as a tool to guide your time with God.

GENEROSITY

"For where your treasure is, there your heart will be also."
Matthew 6:21

CORE TRAIT

- Financial Gifts

WELCOME

Today we will examine the treasures in our lives. When we hear the word *generosity* in the church, sometimes we assume that means only giving money to the church. But in this session we're not going to talk only about giving to the church. We're also going to look to Jesus to see what he says about generosity and how we can become more faithful financial stewards, even in challenging times.

CONNECT

Discuss the following questions with your group to get to know one another better and get the conversation started.

- Which would you prefer, to live near the beach or the mountains? Why?

- When choosing friends, what qualities do you think are most important?

- What adjustments have you made since last week regarding how you spend your time?

- If you had a million dollars to donate to a charity or cause of your choice, which charity or cause would you choose? Why?

In the space that follows, write the names of people you have met and one thing about each of them that you learned in conversation. This will help you remember names and get to know one another a little more.

REFLECT

What do you think of when you hear the word *generosity*? Write your thoughts below.

Now, consider when you have received the generosity of another person. What was the gift? In what ways was it a blessing?

How did receiving the gift of generosity inspire you to be more generous?

1 | VIDEO HIGHLIGHTS: JESUS ON GENEROSITY

"Where your treasure is, there your heart will be also."
Matthew 6:21 CEB

- Do we want to be people whose hearts are ruled by money and objects—or do we want to be people who treasure our relationships with God, family, and friends? What is the treasure that rules your heart?

- We don't have specific Scriptures that address the world's financial crises, but Jesus had much to say about generosity:

"Sell your possessions and give to the poor. Provide purses for yourselves that will not wear out, a treasure in heaven that will never fail, where no thief comes near and no moth destroys."
Luke 12:33

And he told them this parable: "The ground of a certain rich man yielded an abundant harvest. He thought to himself, 'What shall I do? I have no place to store my crops.'

"Then he said, 'This is what I'll do. I will tear down my barns and build bigger ones, and there I will store my surplus grain. And I'll say to myself, 'You have plenty of grain laid up for many years. Take life easy; eat, drink, and be merry.'

"But God said to him, 'You fool! This very night your life will be demanded from you. Then who will get what you have prepared for yourself?'"
Luke 12:16-20

- Jesus isn't saying that we shouldn't plan for the future. He's saying, "You can't take it with you."

- The man in the parable could have been generous, but he put away more than he could ever use while neglecting those who had need at the time.

"From everyone who has been given much, much will be demanded; and from the one who has been entrusted with much, much more will be asked."
Luke 12:48b

"Great gifts mean great responsibilities; greater gifts, greater responsibilities!"
Luke 12:48b *The Message*

- We are blessed so that we can bless others. And when we bless others, we bless Jesus.

- How does our generosity bless Jesus?

"When the Son of Man comes in his glory, and all the angels with him, he will sit on his glorious throne. All the nations will be gathered before him, and he will separate the people one from another as a shepherd separates the sheep from the goats. He will put the sheep on his right and the goats on his left.

"Then the King will say to those on his right, 'Come, you who are blessed by my Father; take your inheritance, the kingdom prepared for you since the creation of the world. For I was hungry and you gave me something to eat, I was thirsty and you gave me something to drink, I was a stranger and you invited me in, I needed clothes and you clothed me, I was sick and you looked after me, I was in prison and you came to visit me.'

"Then the righteous will answer him, 'Lord, when did we see you hungry and feed you, or thirsty and give you something to drink? When did we see you a stranger and invite you in, or needing clothes and clothe you? When did we see you sick or in prison and go to visit you?'

"The King will reply, 'Truly I tell you, whatever you did for one of the least of these brothers and sisters of mine, you did for me.'"
Matthew 25:31-40

- When we reach out and care for others, it is as if we are reaching out and caring for Christ.

- The apostle Paul gave this warning:

People will be lovers of themselves, lovers of money.
2 Timothy 3:2a

- The love of money is really the love of self.

  ○ When we live a life of greed, we place ourselves, rather than God, on the throne.

  ○ Paul even says that when we are greedy, we are idolatrous—we begin to worship money. When we worship money, we are worshiping ourselves.

For of this you can be sure: No immoral, impure or greedy person—such a person is an idolater—has any inheritance in the kingdom of Christ and of God.

Ephesians 5:5

Put to death, therefore, whatever belongs to your earthly nature: sexual immorality, impurity, lust, evil desires and greed, which is idolatry.

Colossians 3:5

- Nothing and no one can, or should, compete with God for our hearts. If money is one's master, God is not.

1 GROUP DISCUSSION

1. Give one example of how someone's generosity changed or impacted your life.

2. Have someone read aloud Proverbs 22:9. What does the Scripture mean to you, and how does it apply to your life?

3. Have someone read aloud Matthew 6:21. What does this Scripture mean to you personally?

4. Assign one or more of the passages below to each person in your group. Then discuss the meaning of each Scripture and how it applies to our lives today.

Zacchaeus—Luke 19:7-9

Rich Young Ruler—Matthew 19:21-22

Poor Widow—Mark 12:41-44

Cheerful Giving—2 Corinthians 9:7

First Things—Matthew 6:33

Growth in Giving—2 Corinthians 8:12

Talents—Matthew 25:15

Blessed to Give—Acts 20:35

2 | VIDEO HIGHLIGHTS: BIBLICAL PRINCIPLES FOR GIVING

Be sure you know the condition of your flocks,
give careful attention to your herds;
for riches do not endure forever,
and a crown is not secure for all generations.
Proverbs 27:23-24

KEY BIBLICAL STEPS[1]

1. Develop a monthly percentage-based spending plan and track all your expenses.

   Application: Take note of Proverbs 27:23-24. Analyze your expenses so that you know what percentage you spend in all categories.

2. Put God first in your living and giving by practicing gratitude and joy.

   Remember this: Whoever sows sparingly will also reap sparingly,
   and whoever sows generously will also reap generously. Each of you
   should give what you have decided in your heart to give, not reluc-
   tantly or under compulsion, for God loves a cheerful giver.

   2 Corinthians 9:6-7

   Application: Thank God daily for all your blessings.

3. Flee from greed and the love of money!

Those who want to get rich fall into temptation and a trap and into many foolish and harmful desires that plunge people into ruin and destruction. For the love of money is a root of all kinds of evil. Some people, eager for money, have wandered away from the faith and pierced themselves with many griefs.

1 Timothy 6:9-10

Application: Begin by paying off all credit card debt and eliminating or limiting credit card use.

4. Seek contentment and simplicity, and live within your means.

"Two things I ask of you, O Lord,
> *do not refuse me before I die:*
Keep falsehood and lies far from me;
> *give me neither poverty nor riches,*
> *but give me only my daily bread.*
Otherwise, I may have too much and disown you
> *and say, 'Who is the Lord?'*
Or I may become poor and steal,
> *and so dishonor the name of my God."*
Proverbs 30:7-9

Application: Begin by being a wise and thrifty shopper. Live simply so that others can simply live.

5. Practice long-range saving and investing habits.

[Jesus asked,] "Suppose one of you wants to build a tower. Will he not first sit down and estimate the cost to see if he has enough to complete it?"

Luke 14:28 NIV 1984

Application: Plan ahead. Create an emergency fund, and save and invest for three to six months of living expenses.

6. Gain [Earn] all you can, save all you can, give all you can.[2]

- Gain [Earn]—*Whatever you do, work at it with all your heart, as working for the Lord, not for human masters, since you know that you will receive an inheritance from the Lord as a reward.*

Colossians 3:23-24a

- Save—*Precious treasure and oil stay in the home of the wise, but fools swallow them up.*

Proverbs 21:20 CEB

- Give—*Every good gift, every perfect gift, comes from above. These gifts come down from the Father, the creator of the heavenly lights, in whose character there is no change at all.*

James 1:17 CEB

Application: Do all the good you can, for all the people you can, for God's glory.

2 GROUP DISCUSSION

1. Review each biblical principle from the video. For each principle, read aloud the principle, its corresponding Scripture, and its application. Discuss the ways each principle might lead to a generous life.

2. How easy or difficult are these principles to put into practice?

3. Do you currently budget or create spending plans? Why or why not?

4. Have you ever been in a situation where you wanted to give but didn't have the financial resources? What was that like?

5. How do these principles prepare us to be generous?

3   VIDEO HIGHLIGHTS: RESET YOUR FINANCIAL LIFE

Command them to do good, to be rich in good deeds, and to be generous and willing to share.
1 Timothy 6:18

- The RESET Tool can help us to rethink our finances and get ourselves realigned financially.

RESET WORKSHEET[3]

What is God calling you to do? We all can improve in our spending, saving, and giving habits. Each of us can reset our personal, spiritual, and financial lives. Perhaps you will want to add other goals to the following.

1. Each day I will simply thank God for all my blessings. My goal for daily Bible reading and prayer will be _____ days each week.

2. I will seek contentment and live within my means each month. My goals will be to develop a monthly cash-flow plan and to track my expenses so that I will spend _____ % of my income.

3. I will seek financial freedom from debt, especially credit card debt. My debt-reduction goal for each month is $ _____.

4. I will seek to wisely manage the gifts God has given me, investing and saving for the future. My savings goal each month is $ _____.

5. I will worship God each week by giving _____% of my income, with tithing (and eventually giving beyond the tithe) being my goal.

- The goal isn't to build up a church budget. The goal is to teach what the Scriptures encourage us to do: share all that we have, including our means, and grow in generosity toward others and God.

3 GROUP DISCUSSION

1. How do you react when a pastor starts to talk about money? Why?

2. Based on what you heard in the video, why does a church need money?

3. Take a few minutes to complete the "RESET Worksheet" (above). How easy or difficult do you think it will be to fulfill each of the statements?

4. How do you think God might be calling you to change your spending habits so that you may give more?

5. Have someone read aloud 1 Timothy 6:18. What would it look like for you to be "rich in good deeds" and "generous and willing to share"?

REVIEW

In this session, the three main points were:

1.

2.

3.

Why is financial freedom important for followers of Jesus?

How is God calling you to give?

CLOSING

In the last video segment, you heard about David, who paid down a huge debt in order to be free to give. Consider what you need to do to your finances to be free to give. Answer the questions below and discuss them with your group.

1. **What is keeping you from being financially generous?**

2. **How can you take control of your finances in order to give more?**

3. **To whom or what would you give more if you had more to give?**

PRAY TOGETHER

Share joys and concerns among your group. Write down anything you are asked to pray for.

Heavenly Father, this can be a challenging topic for many of us. It brings up feelings of confusion, guilt, anger, pain, and even resentment. Help us to see all that we have as gifts from you, and help us to feel encouraged to give all that we can—not because we have to but because we are compelled by love to give. We ask this in your Son's name. Amen.

WALKING IT OUT

- Continue the journey by reflecting on the three main ideas of the session throughout the coming week:

  1. Jesus calls us to be generous with our money.

  2. Financial freedom requires discipline and a plan.

  3. We serve God by keeping our finances in order and giving freely.

- In your personal prayer time:

  ○ give thanks that God has provided for your needs and even blessed you generously;

  ○ acknowledge that you may not have been able to give financially before, but that you want to start the journey now to financial freedom and generosity; and

  ○ praise God for the blessings in your life and the opportunity you have to bless others.

- Give more thought to your spending plan. How is it going? Are you finding extra money? What has been on your heart in this process?

- Spend time each day in personal devotion and prayer. You may want to use *Journey 101 Daily Readings* as a tool to guide your time with God.

SPIRITUAL GIFTS

Each of you should use whatever gift you have received to serve others, as faithful stewards of God's grace in its various forms.
1 Peter 4:10

CORE TRAITS

- Spiritual Gifts
- Talents

WELCOME

Did you know that you are hard-wired with spiritual gifts that are meant to be offered to others, beginning with the Christian community? When we choose to follow Jesus, to serve God, the Lord fills us with the Holy Spirit and places in us gifts. In this session, you'll hear more about spiritual gifts and begin to discern what gifts you might have been given.

CONNECT

Discuss the following questions with your group to get to know one another better and get the conversation started.

- What is the most beautiful place you have ever seen?

- If you had to leave this country, where would you choose to live?

- In what ways has last week's lesson on generosity impacted your life?

- When you were a child, what did you want to be when you grew up?

- What is one thing that people often say you are good at doing?

In the space that follows, write the names of people you have met and one thing about each of them that you learned in conversation. This will help you remember names and get to know one another a little more.

Reflect

As you begin your look at spiritual gifts today, think about the things you do well that come naturally to you. Now think about the things you do well because you learned how to, or developed a particular skill. Finally, think about the things that bring you great joy. Make a list below and circle any similarities between the three lists. Keep those similarities in mind as you participate in today's session.

I am naturally good at . . .

I have learned to be good at . . .

I experience great joy when I . . .

1   VIDEO HIGHLIGHTS: THE BIRTH OF THE CHURCH

Brothers and sisters, I don't want you to be ignorant about spiritual gifts.
1 Corinthians 12:1 CEB

- Spiritual gifts are based on biblical teachings.

"I assure you that whoever believes in me will do the works that I do. They will do even greater works than these because I am going to the Father. I will do whatever you ask for in my name, so that the Father can be glorified in the Son. When you ask me for anything in my name, I will do it.

"If you love me, you will keep my commandments. I will ask the Father, and he will send another Companion, who will be with you forever. This Companion is the Spirit of Truth, whom the world can't receive because it neither sees him nor recognizes him. You know him, because he lives with you and will be with you.

"I won't leave you as orphans. I will come to you."
John 14:12-18 CEB

"The Companion, the Holy Spirit, whom the Father will send in my name, will teach you everything and will remind you of everything I told you."
John 14:26 CEB

"When the Companion comes, whom I will send from the Father—the Spirit of Truth who proceeds from the Father—he will testify about me. You will testify too, because you have been with me from the beginning."
John 15:26-27 CEB

- Jesus made a promise: He will never leave us. He gave us the gift of the Holy Spirit.

While they were eating together, he ordered them not to leave Jerusalem but to wait for what the Father had promised. He said, "This is what you heard from me: John baptized with water, but in only a few days you will be baptized with the Holy Spirit."

As a result, those who had gathered together asked Jesus, "Lord, are you going to restore the kingdom to Israel now?"

Jesus replied, "It isn't for you to know the times or seasons that the Father has set by his own authority. Rather, you will receive power when the Holy Spirit has come upon you, and you will be my witnesses in Jerusalem, in all Judea and Samaria, and to the end of the earth."

Acts 1:4-8 CEB

When Pentecost Day arrived, they were all together in one place. Suddenly a sound from heaven like the howling of a fierce wind filled the entire house where they were sitting. They saw what seemed to be individual flames of fire alighting on each one of them. They were all filled with the Holy Spirit and began to speak in other languages as the Spirit enabled them to speak.

There were pious Jews from every nation under heaven living in Jerusalem. When they heard this sound, a crowd gathered. They were mystified because everyone heard them speaking in their native languages. They were surprised and amazed, saying, "Look, aren't all the people who are speaking Galileans, every one of them? How then can each of us hear them speaking in our native language? Parthians, Medes, and Elamites; as well as residents of Mesopotamia, Judea, and Cappadocia, Pontus and Asia, Phrygia and Pamphylia, Egypt and the regions of Libya bordering Cyrene; and visitors from Rome (both Jews and converts to Judaism), Cretans and Arabs—we hear them declaring the mighty works of God in our own languages!" They were all surprised and bewildered. Some asked each other, "What does this mean?"

Acts 2:1-12 CEB

- The church was born on the day of Pentecost, and we are called to be that church.

- If Jesus is the hope for the world and the church is Jesus' chosen vehicle to bring that hope, then we need to pay attention.

1   GROUP DISCUSSION

1. Have someone read aloud 1 Corinthians 12:7, 12-27. What role do spiritual gifts play in the life of an individual who is seeking to serve God?

2. Refer to the Scriptures from the Video Highlights (John 14:12-18, 26; 15:26-27; Acts 1:4-8; 2:1-12) and discuss the time line from Jesus' promise to send a Companion to the time of the Holy Spirit's arrival at Pentecost. Follow the story and look for insights about what it meant for the disciples to follow Jesus when they knew he was going away.

3. Describe the scene you imagine when you read the story of Pentecost. What does it look like in your mind?

4. If the church is the chosen vehicle to bring hope to the world, how do we go about doing that?

2   VIDEO HIGHLIGHTS: FOUNDATIONAL BIBLE PASSAGES ON SPIRITUAL GIFTS

We have many parts in one body, but the parts don't all have the same function. In the same way, though there are many of us, we are one body in Christ, and individually we belong to each other. We have different gifts that are consistent with God's grace that has been given to us.

Romans 12:4-6*a* CEB

Passage	Who receives the gift?	For what purpose is the gift given?	What gifts are particularly named?
1 Corinthians 12			
Romans 12			
Ephesians 4			
1 Peter 4			

- Each of us receives at least one spiritual gift.

- Spiritual gifts are divine abilities given to every believer through the Holy Spirit.

- Spiritual gifts are given for the common good—to build up the body of Christ and bring glory to God.

- When we come to faith, we are "baptized" by the Spirit. That is when we receive our gifts. No one is excluded.

- How are spiritual gifts different from talents?
  - Talents—God-given abilities that operate under our own power and strength; can be dedicated to God and used to benefit others
  - Spiritual gifts—God-given gifts that are the work of the Holy Spirit; we are the conduits

2 GROUP DISCUSSION

1. Describe the difference between talents and spiritual gifts.

2. How is the example of the body related to the functioning of spiritual gifts within the church?

3 VIDEO HIGHLIGHTS: DEVELOPING AND DISCOVERING SPIRITUAL GIFTS

And serve each other according to the gift each person has received, as good managers of God's diverse gifts.
1 Peter 4:10 CEB

- How to discover your spiritual gifts:
  - Believe that you have gifts. Every believer is given one or more gifts.
  - Pray for God's leading.

- ○ Study the Bible.

- ○ Take a spiritual gifts class.

- ○ Spend time getting to know Jesus.

- ○ Pay attention to the ministries that touch your heart.

- ○ Try different things. Get involved. Do something.

- ○ Judge your experiences—good and bad. Were you effective?

- ○ Ask other people.

- ○ Identify the barriers and excuses that would keep you from discovering and using your gifts, and then remove them.

- Serving God is meant to bring us joy.

- God has uniquely gifted you.

- When you allow the Holy Spirit to work through you to serve others, you bring glory to God.

- When we all do this together, we fully live into Jesus' plan for the church.

3 GROUP DISCUSSION

1. In what ways does the church, and the community beyond its walls, benefit when its members discover, develop, and deploy their spiritual gifts?

2. Have someone read aloud 2 Timothy 1:6-7. What ongoing responsibility do we have with regard to our spiritual gifts? How might we go about doing what Paul advises?

3. Fear of failure is one obstacle that can keep us from using our gifts. Madeleine L'Engle wrote, "If I'm not free to fail, I'm not free to take risks, and everything in life that's worth doing involves a risk of failure. . . . I have to try, but I do not have to succeed. Following Christ has nothing to do with success as the world sees success."[1] If

fear of failure is an obstacle for you, discuss how this quote makes you feel. If fear is not an obstacle, what threatens to keep you from serving God with your gifts?

REVIEW

In this session, the three main points were:

1.

2.

3.

CLOSING

In the last video segment you heard about John, who discovered his spiritual gifts and a greater passion for ministry in the church. Think again about your natural talents and abilities. Consider what gives you great joy. What stirs a passion in you? Fill in the chart below with ideas to get you thinking about your spiritual giftedness.

1. My Natural Abilities and Talents	2. What Brings Me Joy	3. What Stirs a Passion in Me

PRAY TOGETHER

Share joys and concerns among your group. Write down anything you are asked to pray for.

O God, sometimes we are amazed by the fact that you've left your work in the hands of ordinary people like us. And yet, just as Jesus said, you don't leave us as orphans or abandon us but give us the Holy Spirit, who works in us and through us to meet the needs of those around us. God, open our minds and our hearts and our very lives to the truth that we are all gifted people. Help us to discover our gifts and to deploy them for you in service to others. In Christ's name we pray. Amen.

WALKING IT OUT

- Continue the journey by reflecting on the three main ideas of the session throughout the coming week:

  1. The Holy Spirit is present in those who follow Christ.

  2. Every believer has one or more spiritual gifts.

  3. Our spiritual gifts are meant to serve the church and, through the church, the world.

- In your personal prayer time,
  - give thanks that God has gifted you with one or more unique gifts to offer the church,
  - acknowledge that you rely 100 percent on the power of the Holy Spirit as you seek and deploy your gifts for ministry, and
  - praise God for the companionship and comfort of the Holy Spirit.

- Give some more thought to taking a spiritual gifts assessment or class. (See the "Spiritual Gifts Discovery Tool," Ministry Matters, http://www.ministrymatters.com/spiritualgifts/#axzz2OZdrADxJ.)

- Spend time each day in personal devotion and prayer. You may want to use *Journey 101 Daily Readings* as a tool to guide your time with God.

EVANGELISM

Then Jesus came to them and said, "All authority in heaven and on earth has been given to me. Therefore go and make disciples of all nations, baptizing them in the name of the Father and of the Son and of the Holy Spirit, and teaching them to obey everything I have commanded you. And surely I am with you always, to the very end of the age."

Matthew 28:18-20

CORE TRAIT

- Sharing Christ

WELCOME

As you explore serving God in your fifth session today, consider that Jesus has commanded and empowered the church to communicate his message to the world. We are the hands, feet, and voice of Jesus to those in the world who don't know him.

CONNECT

Discuss the following questions with your group to get to know one another better and get the conversation started.

- If you were offered front-row seats to any concert, who would you like to see?

- What is your favorite part of Thanksgiving dinner?

- Which do you think is more important, justice or forgiveness?

- Have you ever witnessed someone evangelizing in a manner that made you feel uncomfortable? How was this person going about sharing the message? Door-to-door? Shouting on a street corner? On television? Other? What about it was off-putting to you?

In the space that follows, write the names of people you have met and one thing about each of them that you learned in conversation. This will help you remember names and get to know one another a little more.

REFLECT

As you approach the topic of evangelism today, consider your faith story. What is important to you about your walk with God? How has following Jesus changed your life? Imagine that you are sharing the gospel of Jesus Christ with someone who has never heard it before. What would you say?

Let me tell you why I follow Jesus. . . .

1 VIDEO HIGHLIGHTS: EVANGELISM PRINCIPLES 1-2

"Neither the one who plants nor the one who waters is anything, but the only one who is anything is God who makes it grow."
1 Corinthians 3:7 CEB

- What is evangelism?
  - Evangelism is sharing the good news of Jesus Christ.
  - *To evangelize is to spread the good news that Jesus Christ died for our sins and was raised from the dead according to the Scriptures, and that as the reigning Lord he now offers the forgiveness of sins and the liberating gift of the Holy Spirit to all who repent and believe. Our Christian presence in the world is indispensable to evangelism, and so is that kind of dialog whose purpose is to listen sensitively in order to understand. But evangelism itself is the proclamation of the historical, biblical Christ as Savior and Lord, with a view to persuading people to come to him personally and so be reconciled to God. In issuing the gospel invitation we have no liberty to conceal the cost of discipleship. Jesus still calls all who would follow him to deny themselves, take up their cross, and identify themselves with his new community. The results of evangelism include obedience to Christ, incorporation into his church and responsible service in the world.[1]*

The Lausanne Covenant

PRINCIPLE #1: CHRISTIAN CONVERSION IS A PROCESS.

- On the way to conversion, most people have twelve to fifteen significant encounters with the gospel message.

Engle Scale of Evangelism[2]

-10	Awareness of the supernatural
-9	No effective knowledge of Christianity
-8	Initial awareness of Christianity
-7	Interest in Christianity
-6	Awareness of basic facts of the gospel
-5	Grasp of implications of the gospel
-4	Positive attitude to the gospel
-3	Awareness of personal need
-2	Challenge and decision to act
-1	Repentance and faith
0	A disciple is born!

+1	Evaluation of decision
+2	Initiation into the church
+3	Become part of the process of making other disciples
+4	Growth in understanding of the faith
+5	Growth in Christian character
+6	Discovery and use of gifts
+7	Christian lifestyle
+8	Stewardship of resources
+9	Prayer
+10	Openness to others/effective sharing of faith and life

- We might be person 3 or 5 or 7 on someone's journey to Christian conversion. This takes the pressure off of us when we feel like we need to convert someone.

PRINCIPLE #2: THE HOLY SPIRIT CREATES HUNGER FOR GOD AND HIGHLIGHTS FELT NEEDS.

- Deep in our hearts there is a longing to know who God is.

    Thou madest us for Thyself, and our heart is restless, until it rest in Thee.[3]

    —Augustine

    He has made everything beautiful in its time. He has also set eternity in the human heart.
    Ecclesiastes 3:11a

- The Holy Spirit creates hunger for God and highlights our felt needs.

    "I have come that they may have life, and have it to the full."
    John 10:10b

- At times in our lives we are especially sensitive and close to the drawings and the wooing of God.

1 | GROUP DISCUSSION

Share with your group:

1. What was your life like before you made the decision to follow Christ?

2. How did you come to know Christ?

3. How has knowing Christ made a difference in your life?

4. As you reflect on coming to faith in Christ, how do you see your conversion as a process?

5. How do you relate to the statistic that it takes twelve to fifteen significant encounters with the gospel for someone to come to faith? What were some of the significant encounters you experienced in your journey toward conversion?

6. Describe a time when you experienced the hunger or need in your heart brought about by the Holy Spirit. Did you struggle for significance? Have questions about the afterlife? Search for purpose?

7. Did you experience a "God-shaped vacuum" in your heart prior to meeting Jesus? If so, with what did you try to fill it?

2 | HIGHLIGHTS: EVANGELISM PRINCIPLES 3-5

The Lord opened her heart to respond to Paul's message.
Acts 16:14b

PRINCIPLE #3: THE HOLY SPIRIT ASSISTS OUR REPENTANCE AND FAITH.

- The Holy Spirit helps us to confess, believe, and trust.

  When the people heard this, they were cut to the heart and said to Peter and the other apostles, "Brothers, what shall we do?"

  Peter replied, "Repent and be baptized, every one of you, in the name of Jesus Christ for the forgiveness of your sins. And you will receive the gift of the Holy Spirit. The promise is for you and your children and for all who are far off—for all whom the Lord our God will call."

  With many other words he warned them; and he pleaded with them, "Save yourselves from this corrupt generation." Those who accepted his message were baptized, and about three thousand were added to their number that day.
  Acts 2:37-41

  One of those listening was a woman from the city of Thyatira named Lydia, a dealer in purple cloth. She was a worshiper of God. The Lord opened her heart to respond to Paul's message.
  Acts 16:14

PRINCIPLE #4: THE HOLY SPIRIT MOVES THROUGH OUR NETWORK OF FAMILY AND FRIENDS.

- The gospel is always spread through relationships and networks of friends.
- The gospel spreads through our families and through our relational networks.

PRINCIPLE #5: THE HOLY SPIRIT REVEALS STRATEGIES.

- The Holy Spirit helps us as we consider our next step in living out Christ's Great Commission.

- The Holy Spirit has strategies to reach people with his life-transforming message. Our job, our joy, is the exciting adventure of following Christ into his strategies.

While they were worshiping the Lord and fasting, the Holy Spirit said, "Set apart for me Barnabas and Saul for the work to which I have called them." So after they had fasted and prayed, they placed their hands on them and sent them off.

Acts 13:2-3

2 GROUP DISCUSSION

1. Have someone read aloud 2 Corinthians 5:16-21. How does Paul summarize the message of the Christian faith? How does knowing and understanding this information help you to articulate your own message to others?

2. Have someone read aloud Acts 1:8. How can we learn to grow in our ability and confidence to share our faith with others?

3. In what ways did the Holy Spirit use your family members or other relationships to reach you?

4. Has the Holy Spirit used you to reach someone in your family or network? If so, how?

5. Have you ever felt led by the Holy Spirit to share the gospel? If so, what strategy or idea did the Holy Spirit lead you to carry out?

3 | VIDEO HIGHLIGHTS: EVANGELISM PRINCIPLES 6-7

PRINCIPLE #6: THE FRUIT OF EVANGELISM CAN BE MEASURED.

- Luke cared about numbers and included such details throughout the Book of Acts.

Those who accepted his message were baptized, and about three thousand were added to their number that day.
Acts 2:41

And the Lord added to their number daily those who were being saved.
Acts 2:47b

But the word of God continued to increase and spread.
Acts 12:24 NIV 1984

- The Holy Spirit draws people to Christ, and the fruit of evangelism is measurable.

- It is God's heart—God's desire—that churches grow.

PRINCIPLE #7: THE HOLY SPIRIT EMPOWERS OUR WITNESS.

- Evangelism is not about what *we* can do; it's about what God can do through ordinary people like us.

"But you will receive power when the Holy Spirit comes on you; and you will be my witnesses in Jerusalem, and in all Judea and Samaria, and to the ends of the earth."
Acts 1:8

- One of life's greatest adventures is to be led by the Holy Spirit to share the life-changing message of Jesus with others.

- The power of the Holy Spirit helps us in our witness.

- Evangelism is one of the most profound ways for us to love and serve God.

For Christ's love compels us, because we are convinced that one died for all, and therefore all died. And he died for all, that those who live should no longer live for themselves but for him who died for them and was raised again.

2 Corinthians 5:14-15

3 GROUP DISCUSSION

1. Identify a person in your life that you would like to see have a close, personal relationship with Christ. Drawing upon today's teaching, name one or more actions you can take in the coming week that will move you closer to sharing your faith with this person.

2. Do you agree that the fruit of evangelism matters, that it is quantifiable? Do numbers really matter? Why?

3. Take turns reading aloud Acts 1–2. Point out where evangelism is happening in the story. List any numbers noted about people coming to believe. What do we learn about evangelism in this story?

4. Brainstorm some strategies for sharing your faith. What places do you frequently visit? Who crosses your path regularly? How can you be prepared to share your faith when the Holy Spirit nudges you?

5. How will you serve God through the adventure of evangelism?

REVIEW

In this session, the seven principles of evangelism were:

1.

2.

3.

4.

5.

6.

7.

CLOSING

In the final video segment you heard how Jeff was instrumental in helping the man from Africa come to faith in Christ on an airplane. Consider who has been instrumental in your journey of faith and for whom you might become that instrumental person. List the people for whom you thank God—those who led you to Jesus. Then, list the people you have influence over or come in contact with—those for whom you might be that monumental influence.

Thank God for. . . .

Lord, use me to reach. . . .

PRAY TOGETHER

Share joys and concerns among your group. Write down anything you are asked to pray for.

O God, we pray that these words might fall like seeds on receptive soil. Inspire us, transform our thinking, and fill us with new strategies so that others might come to know you. We thank you for the presence and power of the Holy Spirit, and for enabling us to be your witnesses. Lord, what a joy, what a thrill, what a responsibility you have given to us. Fill us afresh with your love and power. May the love of Christ compel us. For it's in his name we pray. Amen.

WALKING IT OUT

- Continue the journey by reflecting on the seven principles of the session throughout the coming week:

  1. Christian conversion is a process.

  2. The Holy Spirit creates hunger for God and highlights felt needs.

  3. The Holy Spirit assists our repentance and faith.

  4. The Holy Spirit moves through our network of family and friends.

  5. The Holy Spirit reveals strategies.

  6. The fruit of evangelism can be measured.

  7. The Holy Spirit empowers our witness.

- In your personal prayer time:
  - give thanks for the people God placed in your life to tell you about God's love;
  - ask God to place you in someone's life this week to be a blessing and share the message of the gospel. Be prepared to pray with them to entrust their lives to Christ and seek to follow him daily; and
  - praise God for the awesome adventure of life with him.

- Give more thought to the people with whom you feel led to share the gospel. Practice writing out your God story and imagine what you will say about your beliefs and how the gospel has changed your life.

- Spend time each day in personal devotion and prayer. You may want to use *Journey 101 Daily Readings* as a tool to guide your time with God.

SERVING GOD THROUGH SOCIAL SERVICE

"Peace be with you. As the Father sent me, so I am sending you."
John 20:21 CEB

CORE TRAIT

- Service to Others

WELCOME

Welcome to our final session of *Journey 101: Serving God*. We have explored what it means to serve God, discovered things that are important to God, and looked to Jesus as the model for serving. In this last session we'll discuss social service—how we serve others in our communities and the world.

CONNECT

Discuss the following questions with your group to get to know one another better and get the conversation started.

- Share your craziest "trying to get to church" story.

- If you could vacation anywhere in the world, where would you choose? Why?

- If it were possible and you had the means to do something wildly generous—anything—what would you choose to do?

- What do you see as needs in your community?

In the space that follows, write the names of people you have met during these sessions and one thing about each of them that you learned in conversation. Do you feel that you know one another better now than when the study began?

REFLECT

Here, at the end of your study, reflect on what you have learned about serving God. How have your thoughts changed or your passions shifted? Now that you have a deeper understanding of serving God, take a final assessment of your willingness and availability to serve by marking the scale below and completing the sentence.

Sign me up!   Let me get back to you...   I can't do that!

| 1 | 2 | 3 | 4 | 5 | 6 | 7 | 8 | 9 | 10 |

Serving God means . . .

1   VIDEO HIGHLIGHTS: THE CALL TO BE SALT AND LIGHT

Again Jesus said, "Peace be with you! As the Father has sent me, I am sending you."

John 20:21

- What Jesus was he still is, and what Jesus did he still does. But now he does it through you.

  *"You are the salt of the earth. . . . You are the light of the world. . . .
  Let your light shine before others, that they may see your good deeds
  and glorify your Father in heaven."*

  Matthew 5:13, 14, 16

- We are to show the love and light of Christ in our words and our actions, being attentive to the needs of others and offering a helping hand.

- Historically, many heroes of the faith have heeded the call to be salt and light in a broken and hurting world, bringing God's light to oppressive social conditions such as injustice, racism, poverty, and illiteracy. Two examples are John Wesley and William Wilberforce.[1]

- Everyday heroes inspire us as well—people who give their time, gifts, and resources to make a difference in the world.

- Jesus calls us to join them, to be salt and light in the world.

1   GROUP DISCUSSION

1. Reflect on this statement: "What Jesus was he still is, and what Jesus did he still does. But now he does it through you." What do you think of this idea? How does Jesus do what he did, even today, through you?

2. Have someone read aloud Matthew 5:13-16. What does it mean to be the "salt of the earth"?

3. What does it mean to be the "light of the world"?

4. The video offers John Wesley and William Wilberforce as examples of men who let their light shine. Can you name some other persons who were committed to the work of Jesus, even when it became difficult?

5. Who are the local heroes in your area who shine the light of Christ in their lives? What is unique about the way they live out their faith?

2 VIDEO HIGHLIGHTS: CHOOSING TO SERVE

"Let your light shine before others, that they may see your good deeds and glorify your Father in heaven."
Matthew 5:16

- We have two options in how we will choose to relate to the world as Christians:

    1. Withdraw and retreat.

        ○ This means to withdraw from the world's needs and retreat to the safety of a community where everyone believes and practices the same things.

        ○ This describes a church that has become a spiritual safe house where people seek to separate from the world's corruptions and compromises.

    2. Engage the world in service.

        ○ This means to find effective ways to engage the world in meaningful and costly service following the example of Jesus.

        ○ This describes a church that seeks to be salt and light in the world.

- Jesus calls us to both social service and social action.
    - Social service—helping to alleviate a critical need
    - Social action—the effort to eradicate the reason the need exists

    Example: One organization delivers food to hungry people, while another organization works to remove the causes of hunger. Both tasks of social service (bringing emergency food) and social action (working to eradicate hunger) are expressions of being "salt and light" to a world in crisis.

- There are so many needs in our world, and so many ways to follow Jesus to the needs of people that he deeply loves and cares for.
- Christian discipleship—learning to love and serve those Jesus loves
- As followers of Jesus, we too are called to serve others in our path, using our gifts and resources to meet their needs.
- Choosing to engage the world in meaningful and costly service following the example of Jesus is one of the most meaningful and rewarding choices you will ever make.

2 GROUP DISCUSSION

1. Discuss the "withdraw and retreat" mentality. What makes us want to form a spiritual safe house?

2. Discuss the "engage in social service" church. What are some examples of churches that are known for their engagement in Christian service?

3. Discuss the difference between social service and social action. Name some examples of each.

4. Do you think one is better than the other? Why or why not?

5. When you consider serving in some way, what kind of service immediately comes to mind?

6. Would you say your heart leans more toward social service or social action? Why do you think this is so?

7. Tell a story about a time you were moved by serving others or by someone serving you.

---

3 │ VIDEO HIGHLIGHTS: CHANGING THE WORLD ONE ACT OF LOVE AT A TIME

Remember those in prison as if you were their fellow prisoners, and those who are mistreated as if you yourselves were suffering.
Hebrews 13:3 NIV 1984

- Wonderful ministries are being carried out by churches and Christians all over the country and world!
- Sometimes our efforts of sharing the gospel are hampered by perceptions of those outside the church. The occasional misdeeds of institutional Christianity have produced among some people a disdain for the message of faith.
- Some would say that the church within our culture has lost the right to be heard.
- Those on the outside of faith would be far more interested in our faith if they witnessed Christians acting more like Jesus.

- To effectively serve others, we need to become more like Jesus.

- How are you and your church community doing in following God's call to be salt and light in your community?

- It is far better to do something, even if it is a little, and allow God to multiply it, than to do nothing.

- *Small things done with great love will change the world.*[2]

- We can change the world—one small act of love at a time.

- What small act can you take this week that will begin to make that change in the world? What bigger dream do you have for a lasting difference?

3   GROUP DISCUSSION

1. Have someone read aloud Hebrews 13:3. Discuss the implications this verse would have on your life if you lived it out.

2. In what ways does the church lose its credibility when the "occasional misdeeds" of some Christians pop up in the news?

3. How can the church earn the right to be heard?

4. In the video, Jeff posed the question, "How are you and your church community doing in following God's call to be salt and light in your community?" Discuss this question as honestly as you can.

5. What is your church doing well that you can build upon in order to serve more people more effectively?

6. What does your church need to do to become more like Jesus?

7. Discuss the paraphrased quote of Mother Teresa. How do small things done in love change the world?

8. Discuss Jeff's final questions: What small act can you take this week that will begin to make that change in the world? What big dream do you have for a lasting difference?

REVIEW

In this session, the three main points were:

1.

2.

3.

Why do we serve God?

How do we serve God?

CLOSING

In the last video segment you heard the story about a New York cabbie who offered an inspired and eloquent homily of what the church would do if it were like Jesus. What would it look like for you to dream big about the ministries of your church? Answer the following questions and then share with your group.

1. **How is the Holy Spirit stirring in you through this topic today?**

2. **How might you dream big about what God can do in and through you to serve others?**

3. **Make a commitment to pray, discern, and talk with others about joining or starting a ministry of service.**

PRAY TOGETHER

Share joys and concerns among your group. Write down anything you are asked to pray for.

Heavenly Father, thank you for your great love for us. Thank you for inviting us into your work in the world. We know, Lord, that we are small. But by your power we can do great things. Create in us a vision for ministry. Show us how you would have us serve. Give us the courage to step out of our comfort zones. Forgive us when we withdraw and retreat from your call. Help us to be brave as we follow Jesus. In Jesus' name. Amen.

WALKING IT OUT

- Continue the journey by reflecting on the three main ideas of the session throughout the coming week:

  1. Jesus calls his followers to be salt and light.

  2. Choosing to serve God is one of the most meaningful choices you can ever make.

  3. We can change the world with one act of love at a time.

- In your personal prayer time,
  - give thanks that God has called you into ministry;
  - acknowledge that you may not know exactly how or when to serve God and ask God to open doors of service and give you courage to serve; and
  - praise God for the example of Jesus Christ who shows us the way to know him, to love him, and to serve him perfectly.

- Give more thought to the ways that the Spirit is stirring in you. What gifts and talents or interests do you have? How could those things help you find a place to serve?
  - Spend time each day in personal devotion and prayer. You may want to use the *Journey 101 Daily Readings* as a tool to guide your time with God.

NOTES

Session 1: How and Why We Serve God

1. John Wesley, "On Visiting the Sick," *The Works of John Wesley* (Nashville: Abingdon, 1986), 3:387–88.

2. Frederick Buechner, *Wishful Thinking* (New York: HarperOne, 1993), 95.

Session 2: Serving with Time

1. John Ortberg, *The Life You've Always Wanted* (Grand Rapids: Zondervan, 2002), 76.

2. Richard Swenson, *Margin: Restoring Emotional, Physical, Financial, and Time Reserves to Overloaded Lives* (Colorado Springs: NavPress, 2004), 155–61.

3. Dietrich Bonhoeffer, *Life Together* (New York: Harper&Brothers, 1954), 99.

Session 3: Generosity

1. These key biblical principles were taken from Scripture and have been fleshed out by Rev. Dr. Clayton Smith of The United Methodist Church of the Resurrection.

2. This catchphrase is often used to sum up John Wesley's teachings on money.

3. The RESET Worksheet was created by Rev. Dr. Clayton Smith of The United Methodist Church of the Resurrection.

Session 4: Spiritual Gifts

1. Madeleine L'Engle, *Choices for Graduates* (Grand Rapids: Baker, 1988), 26.

Session 5: Evangelism

1. Lausanne Covenant, http://www.emeu.net/pdf/lausanne_covenant.pdf.

2. Engle Scale of Evangelism adapted from James F. Engel and Wilbert Norton, *What's Gone Wrong with the Harvest?* (Grand Rapids: Zondervan: 1975).

3. Augustine, *The Confessions of Saint Augustine* 1.1.1.

Session 6: Serving God Through Social Service

1. Robert Isaac Wilberforce and Samuel Wilberforce, *The Life of William Wilberforce*, (Philadelphia: Henry Perkins, 1839), 65.

2. Steve Sjogren, *Conspiracy of Kindness: A Unique Approach to Sharing the Love of Jesus*, rev. ed. (Regal: Ventura, Calif., 2010), 239.